AH SWEET MYSTERY OF LIFE

Words by ...
Music by VICTOR HERB...

THE ABA DABA HONEYMOON

Words and Music by ARTHUR FIELDS
and WALTER DONOVAN

The Aba Daba Honeymoon - 2 - 1

AFTER THE BALL

Words and Music by CHARLES K HARRIS

After The Ball - 2 - 1

AFTER YOU'VE GONE

Words and Music by HENRY CREAMER
and TURNER LAYTON

© 1918 Morley Music Co Inc, USA
Francis Day & Hunter Ltd, London WC2H 0EA

ALEXANDER'S RAGTIME BAND

Words and Music by IRVING BERLIN

Alexander's Ragtime Band - 4 - 1

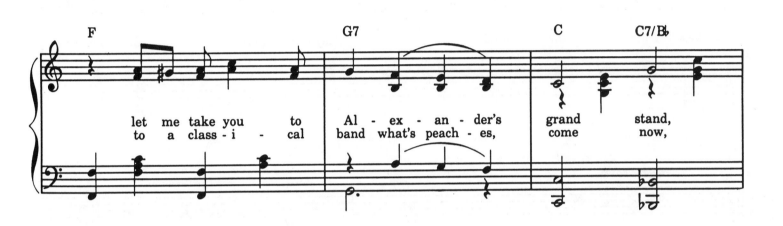

Chorus:

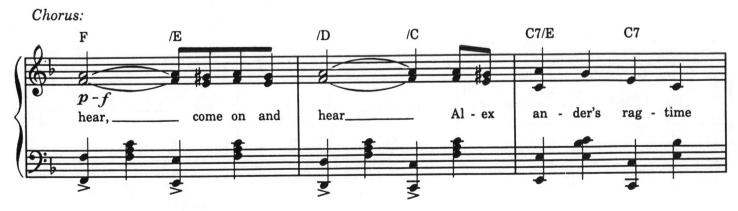

Alexander's Ragtime Band - 4 - 2

ALICE BLUE GOWN

Words by JOSEPH McCARTHY
Music by HARRY TIERNEY

AVALON

Words by AL JOLSON and B.G.DeSYLVA
Music by VINCENT ROSE

Avalon - 3 - 1

24

ANCHORS AWEIGH

Words and Music by
CAPT. ALFRED H. MILES, U.S.N. (RET.)
and CHARLES A. ZIMMERMANN

BALLIN' THE JACK

Words and Music by
JIM BURRIS and CHRIS SMITH

Ballin' the Jack - 3 - 1

BECAUSE

French Words by GUY d'HARDELOT
English Words by EDWARD TESCHEMACHER
Music by GUY d'HARDELOT

A BICYCLE BUILT FOR TWO
(Daisy Bell)

Words and Music by
HARRY DACRE

Waltz tempo

There is a flow-er with-in my heart, Dai - sy,
We will go "Tan-dem" as man and wife, Dai - sy,
I will stand by you in "wheel" or woe, Dai - sy,

Dai - sy! Plant-ed one day by a glanc-ing dart,
Dai - sy! "Ped'-ling" a-way down the road of life,
Dai - sy! You'll be the bell(e) which I'll ring, you know!

A Bicycle Built For Two - 3-1

A BIRD IN A GILDED CAGE

Words by ARTHUR J. LAMB
Music by HARRY VON TILZER

*) Symbols for Guitar, Chords for Ukulele and Banjo

THE BAND PLAYED ON

Valse moderato

Words by JOHN F. PALMER
Music by CHARLES B. WARD

Ca - sey would waltz with a straw - ber - ry blonde, And The Band Played On, _____ He'd glide cross the floor with the girl he a - dor'd, and The Band Played On, _____ But his brain was so

The Band Played On - 2 - 1

BE MY LITTLE BABY BUMBLEBEE

Words by STANLEY MURPHY
Music by HENRY I. MARSHALL

THE BELLS OF ST. MARY'S

Words by DOUGLAS FURBER
Music by EMMETT ADAMS

sound of the sea, I know you'll be wait - ing, yes wait - ing for me. The
voi - ces shall sing, for you and me dear - est, the wed - ding bells ring.

bells of St Ma - ry's, ah hear, they are call - ing the young loves, the

true loves who come from the sea, and so my be - lov - èd, when

BILL BAILEY, WON'T YOU PLEASE COME HOME?

Words and Music by HUGHIE CANNON

Bill Bailey, Won't You Please Come Home - 2 - 1

BY THE LIGHT OF THE SILVERY MOON

Lyrics by ED MADDEN
Music by GUS EDWARDS

By The Light Of The Silvery Moon - 3 - 1

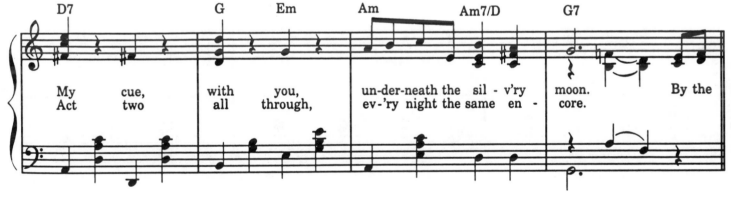

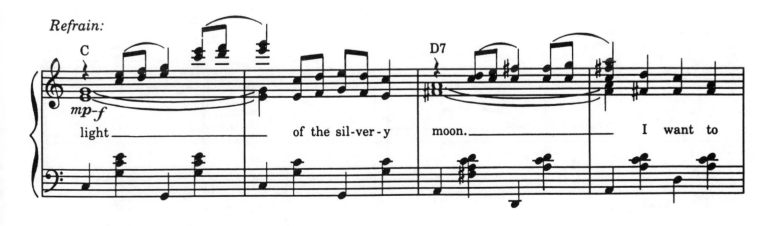

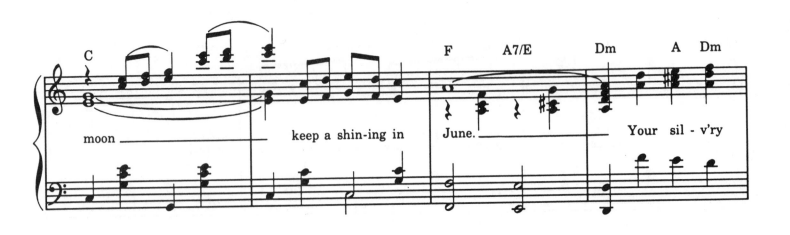

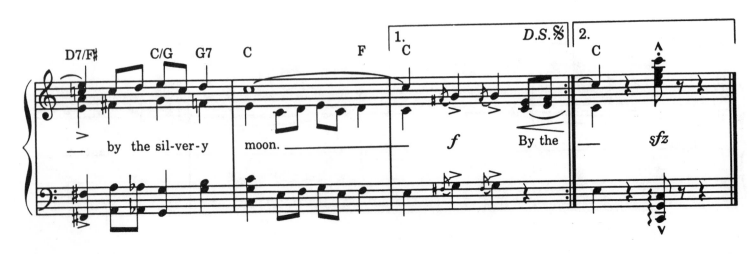

BY THE BEAUTIFUL SEA

Words by HAROLD R. ATTERIDGE
Music by HARRY CARROLL

Brightly

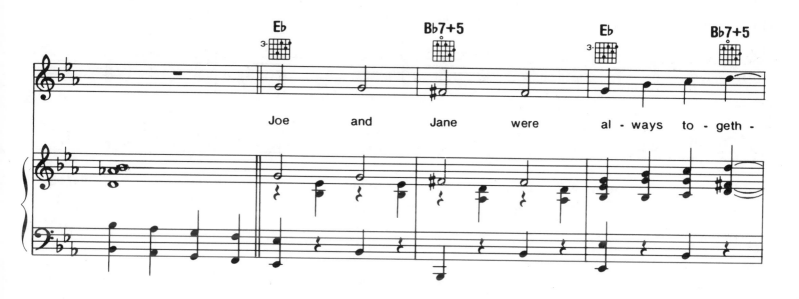

Joe and Jane were al - ways to - geth -

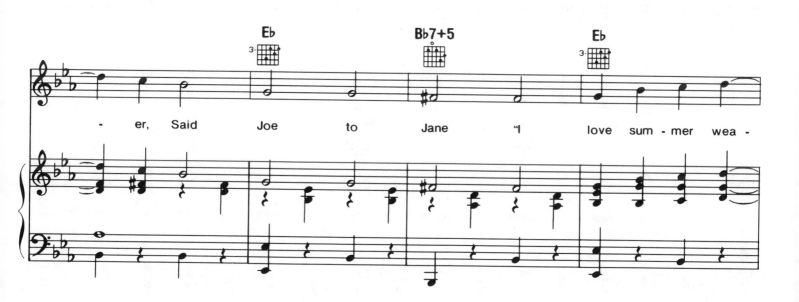

- er, Said Joe to Jane "I love sum - mer wea -

COME, JOSEPHINE IN MY FLYING MACHINE
(Up She Goes!)

Words by ALFRED BRYAN
Music by FRED FISCHER

CUDDLE UP A LITTLE CLOSER, LOVEY MINE

Lyric by O. A. HAUERBACH
Music by KARL HOSCHNA

grew more cold,— And he grew more bold, Till she tho't that they had bet-ter
Es - qui - maux,— 'Mid the ice and snow, Has no steam-heat when he comes to

go.————— But al - tho' he heard,— He not e - ven stirred. On - ly
call.————— Not a sin - gle glim, So its up to him,— To

mur - mured in tones soft and low.—————
whis - per in sum - mer or fall."—————

CHORUS. *Moderato.*

Cud - dle up a lit - tle clos - er, Lov - ey mine.

p-f a tempo.

Cud - dle up and be my lit - tle cling - ing vine.

Like to feel your cheek so ros - y,

Like to make you com - fy, co - zy. Cause I love from head to

toe - sie Lov - ey mine. mine.

CANADIAN CAPERS

Words by EARL BURTNETT
Music by GUS CHANDLER,
BERT WHITE and HENRY COHEN

CHINATOWN MY CHINATOWN

Words by WILLIAM JEROME
Music by JEAN SCHWARTZ

1. When the town is fast a - sleep,_____
2. Stran - gers tak - ing in the sights,_____

and it's mid - night in the sky,_____
pig - tails fly - ing here and there;_____

COME TO THE BALL

Words by ADRIAN ROSS
Music by LIONEL MONCKTON

DANNY BOY
(Londonderry Air)

Words by
FREDERICK EDWARD WEATHERLY

THE DARKTOWN STRUTTERS' BALL

Words and Music by SHELTON BROOKS

DOWN BY THE OLD MILL STREAM

Words and Music by TELL TAYLOR

Down By The Old Mill Stream - 3 - 1

80

hair has turned to sil - ver, the gold has fad - ed too; but
you and I are sweet-hearts, the same as days of yore; al -

still I will re - mem - ber, where I first met you.
though we've been to - geth - er, for - ty years or more. Down by the

Chorus:

Valse lento

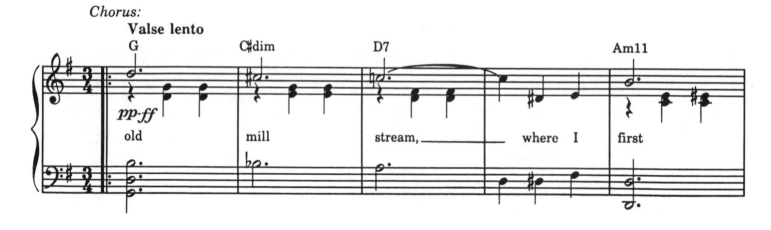

old mill stream, where I first

met you, with your eyes of

THE ENTERTAINER

Words and Music by SCOTT JOPLIN

EVERY DAY IS LADIES' DAY WITH ME

Words by HENRY BLOSSOM
Music by VICTOR HERBERT

EVERYBODY'S DOIN' IT NOW

Words and Music by IRVING BERLIN

FASCINATION

Words by JEAN REYNOLDS DAVIS
Music by F. D. MARCHETTI

FOR ME AND MY GAL

Words by EDGAR LESLIE and E RAY GOETZ
Music by GEORGE W MEYER

joy,_____ he's the luck - i - est boy,_____ in his wed-ding ar -

sight_____ as the fam-ilies u - nite._____ Gee! it makes the boy

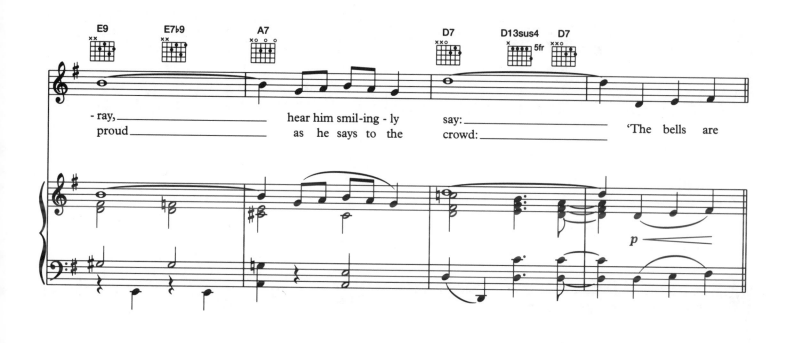

- ray,_____ hear him smil-ing - ly say:_____ 'The bells are

proud_____ as he says to the crowd:_____

ring - ing_____ for me and my gal,_____ the birds are

THE FLORAL DANCE

By KATIE MOSS

GLOW WORM

Words by LILLA CAYLEY ROBINSON
Music by PAUL LINCKE

When the night falls si-lent-ly,___ the night falls si-lent-ly___ on for-ests
"Lit-tle glow-worm, tell me pray,___ oh glow-worm, tell me pray,___ how did you

dream-ing, Lov-ers wan-der forth to see,___ they wan-der
kin-dle, Lamps that by the break of day,___ that by the

forth to see___ the bright stars gleam-ing; And lest they should
break of day,___ must fade and dwin-dle?" "Ah this se-cret,

110

GIVE MY REGARDS TO BROADWAY

Words and Music by GEORGE M. COHAN

Give my re-gards to Broad-way, Re-mem-ber me to Her-ald Square;

Tell all the gang, at For-ty Sec-ond Street that I will soon be there.

Give My Regards To Broadway - 2 - 1

GOOD-BYE BROADWAY, HELLO FRANCE!

Words by C. FRANCIS RIESNER and BENNY DAVIS
Music by BILLY BASKETTE

* Name of any City may be Substituted for Broadway if desired.

HAIL! HAIL! THE GANG'S ALL HERE

Words and Music by THEODORE MORSE
and ARTHUR SULLIVAN

* Optional: "deuce", "heck", &c

HARRIGAN

Words and Music by GEORGE M. COHAN

HE'D HAVE TO GET UNDER-
GET OUT AND GET UNDER
(To Fix Up His Automobile)

Words by GRANT CLARKE and EDGAR LESLIE
Music by MAURICE ABRAHAMS

John-ny O' Con - nor bought an au-to-mo-bile, ___ He took his sweet-heart for a
Mill-ion-aire Wil - son said to John-ny one day, ___ Your lit-tle sweet-heart don't ap-

ride one Sun - day, John-ny was togged ___ up in his best Sun-day clothes, ___
pre - ci - ate you, I have a daugh - ter who is hun-gry for love, ___

HAS ANYBODY HERE SEEN KELLY?

Words and Music by C. W. MURPHY, WILL LETTERS,
JOHN CHARLES MOORE and WILLIAM J. McKENNA

HINKY DINKY PARLEY-VOO

Traditional

HELLO! MY BABY

Words by IDA EMERSON
Music by JOSEPH E. HOWARD

With a Bounce

Hel-lo, my ba-by, hel-lo my hon-ey,

Hel-lo, my rag-time gal! Send me a kiss by

wire; Ba-by my heart's on fire!

Hello! My Baby - 2 - 1

F
G7
If you re - fuse me, hon - ey, you'll lose me, Then you'll be left a -
C7
Cdim
C7
lone; Oh, ba - by, tel - e - phone and tell me I'm your
1.
F
F♯dim
Gm7
C7+
2.
F
own. Hel-lo! Hel - lo! Hel-lo there! own.

I DON'T CARE

Words by JEAN LENOX
Music by HARRY O. SUTTON

I LOVE A PIANO

(From the Stage Production "Stop! Look! Listen!)

Words and Music by IRVING BERLIN

I LOVE THE MOON

Words and Music by PAUL A RUBENS

I LOVE YOU TRULY

Words and Music by CARRIE JACOBS-BOND

I WANT A GIRL
(Just Like The Girl That Married Dear Old Dad)

Words by WILLIAM DILLON
Music by HARRY Von TILZER

I WONDER WHO'S KISSING HER NOW

Words by WILL HOUGH and FRANK ADAMS
Music by JOSEPH EDGAR HOWARD

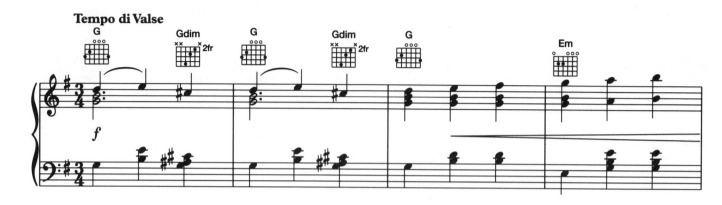

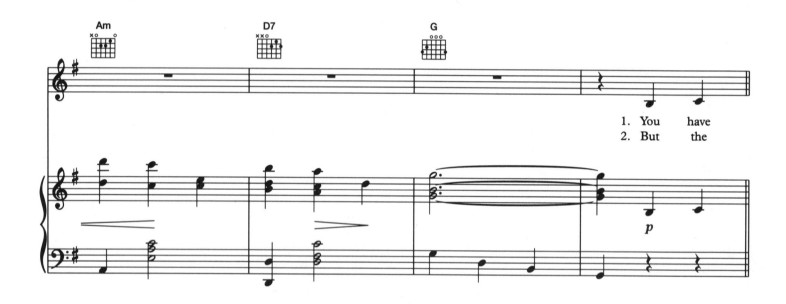

1. You have
2. But the

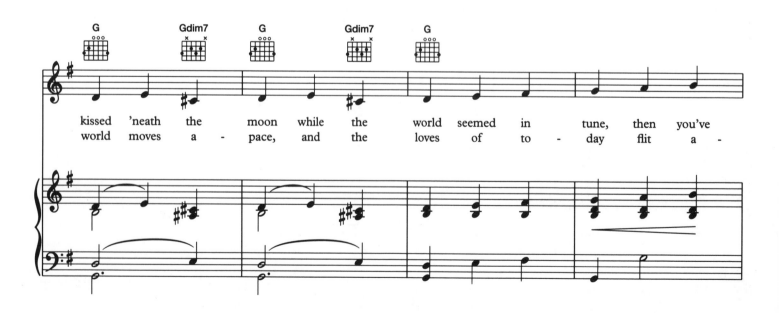

kissed 'neath the moon while the world seemed in tune, then you've
world moves a - pace, and the world loves of to - day flit a -

I'M ALWAYS CHASING RAINBOWS

Words by JOSEPH McCARTHY
Music by HARRY CARROLL

I'M FOREVER BLOWING BUBBLES

Words and Music by
JAAN KENBROVIN and JOHN KELLETTE

sky,   then like my dreams, they fade and die.

For - tune's al - ways hid - ing,_____ I've looked ev - ery -

- where,_____ I'm for-ev - er blow - ing bub - bles,_____ pret-ty

bub - bles in the air._____ air._____

I'M SHY MARY ELLEN, I'M SHY

Words and Music by
CHARLES RIDGEWELL and GEORGE A STEVENS

154

I'M SORRY I MADE YOU CRY

Words and Music by N. J. CLESI

I'm Sorry I Made You Cry - 2 - 1

I'm Sorry I Made You Cry - 2 - 2

IF I KNOCK THE 'L' OUT OF KELLY

Words by SAM M. LEWIS and JOE YOUNG
Music by BERY GRANT

Tim - o - thy Kel - ly, who owned a big
Tim - o - thy Kel - ly, looked up at the

store, want - ed his name paint - ed ov - er the door.
sign. He told Pat Clan - cy, "That's no name of mine.

I'VE GOT RINGS ON MY FINGERS

(A/K/A Mumbo, Jumbo Jijjiboo J. O'Shea)

Words by WESTON and BARNES
Music by MAURICE SCOTT

IDA, SWEET AS APPLE CIDER

Words by EDDIE LEONARD
Music by EDDIE MUNSON

1. In the re - gion where the ros - es al - ways bloom,_____
2. When the moon comes steal - ing up be - hind the hill,_____

breath - ing out up - on the air their sweet per - fume,_____
ev - 'ry-thing a - round me seems so calm and still,_____

Ida, Sweet As Apple Cider - 5 - 1

Ida, Sweet As Apple Cider - 5 - 2

Ida, Sweet As Apple Cider - 5 - 3

Refrain:

I - da!_____ sweet as ap - ple ci - der,_____ sweet - er_____ than all I know,_____ come out!_____ in the silv - 'ry moon - light,_____ of love we'll whis - per,_____ so soft and low!_____

IF YOU WERE THE ONLY GIRL IN THE WORLD

Words by CLIFFORD GREY
Music by NAT D AYER

just made for two, with no-thing to mar our joy.

I would say such won-der-ful things to you, there would be such

won-der-ful things to do, if you I were the on - ly girl in the world, and

I you were the on - ly boy. If boy.

D.C.

IN MY MERRY OLDSMOBILE

Words by VINCENT BRYAN
Music by GUS EDWARDS

In My Merry Oldsmobile - 3 - 1

when they go for a spin, you know, She tries to
day they spoon to the en - gine's tune, Their hon - ey -

learn the au - to, so He lets her steer while he
moon will hap - pen soon, He'll win Lu - cile with his

gets her ear, And whis - pers soft and low; Come a -
Olds - mo - bile And then he'll fond - ly croon; Come a -

CHORUS

way with me Lu - cile _____ In my mer - ry Olds - mo -

In My Merry Oldsmobile - 3 - 3

IN THE SHADE OF THE OLD APPLE TREE

Words by HARRY H. WILLIAMS
Music by EGBERT VAN ALSTYNE

In The Shade Of The Old Apple Tree - 2 - 1

In The Shade Of The Old Apple Tree - 2 - 2

INDIAN SUMMER

Words by AL DUBIN
Music by VICTOR HERBERT

Indian Summer - 2 - 1

Indian Summer - 2 - 2

IT'S A LONG LONG WAY TO TIPPERARY

Words and Music by JACK JUDGE
and HARRY WILLIAMS

IN THE GOOD OLD SUMMERTIME

Words by REN SHIELDS
Music by GEORGE EVANS

JA-DA

Words and Music by BOB CARLETON
Revised Lyric and Arrangement by
NAN WYNN and KEN LANE

THE JAPANESE SANDMAN

Words by RAYMOND B. EGAN
Music by RICHARD A. WHITING

The Japanese Sandman - 2 - 1

The Japanese Sandman - 2 - 2

JUST BECAUSE SHE MADE DEM GOO-GOO EYES

Words and Music by JOHN QUEEN
and HUGHIE CANNON

Just Because She Made Dem Goo-Goo Eyes - 2 - 1

got to stand a fine" he lost his job, ————— for quite a while. —————
blow the road right here, if you'll be mine, ————— if you'll be mine. —————
eat with-out no dough, so here I am, ————— out in the snow."

Chorus, Moderato

Just be-cause she made them Goo-Goo eyes ————— I

thought I'd won a home and copp'd a prize ————— She

is the best what is ————— and I need her in my biz, Just be-cause she

makes them Goo-Goo eyes. ————— eyes. —————

JOHNSON RAG

Lyrics by JACK LAWRENCE
Music by GUY HALL and HENRY KLEINKAUF

191

KEEP THE HOME FIRES BURNING

Words by LENA GUILBERT FORD
Music by IVOR NOVELLO

KISS ME AGAIN

Words by HENRY BLOSSOM
Music by VICTOR HERBERT

K-K-K-KATY

Words and Music by GEOFFREY O'HARA

LET ME CALL YOU SWEETHEART

Words by BETH SLATER WHITSON
Music by LEO FRIEDMAN

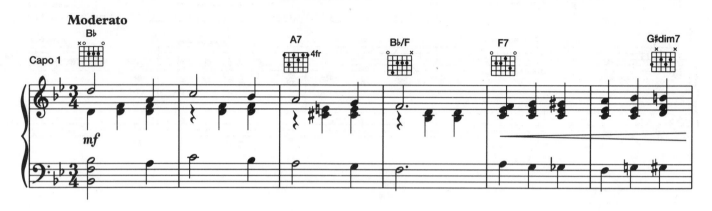

1. I am dream - ing dear, of you,
2. Long - ing for you all the while,

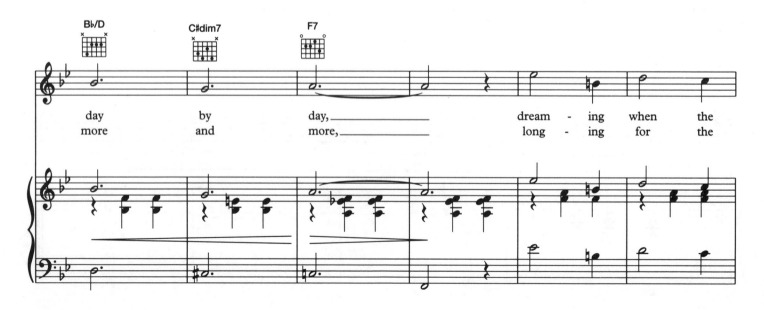

day by day,_____ dream - ing when the
more by and more,_____ long - ing for the

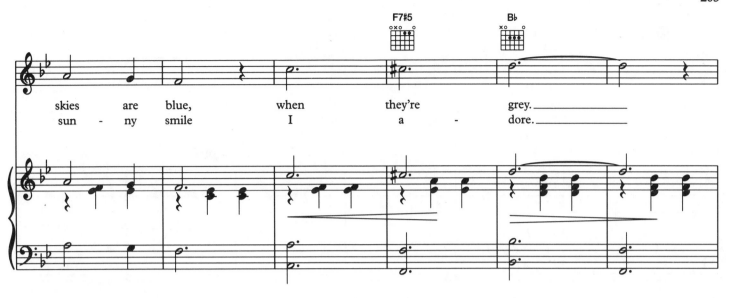

skies are blue, when they're grey._____
sun - ny smile I a - dore._____

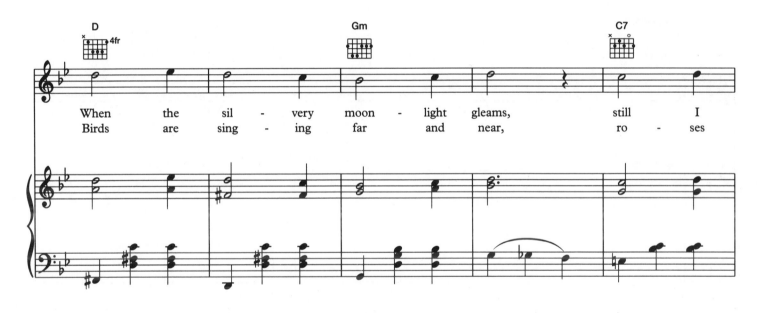

When the sil - very moon - light gleams, still I
Birds are sing - ing far and near, ro - ses

wan - der on in dreams, in a land of
bloom - ing ev - ery - where, you a - lone my

love,   it   seems,   just   with   you._____
heart   can   cheer,   you,   just   you._____

Let   me   call   you   sweet - heart   I'm   in   love

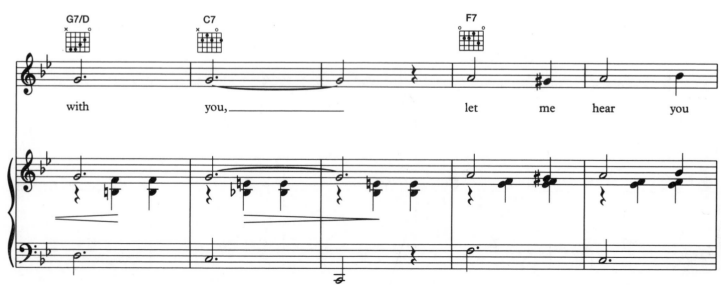

with   you,_____   let   me   hear   you

LET THE REST OF THE WORLD GO BY

Words by J KEIRN BRENNAN
Music by ERNEST R BALL

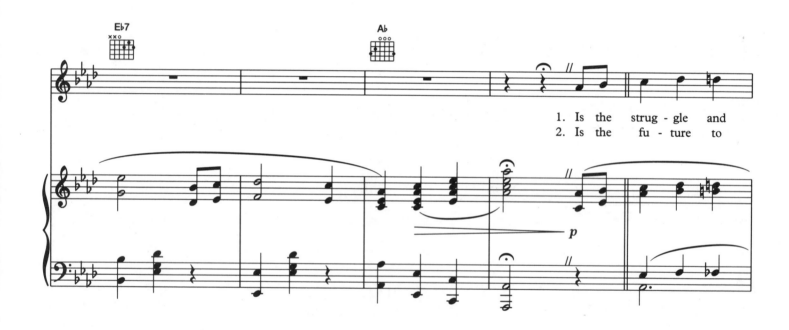

1. Is the strug - gle and
2. Is the fu - ture to

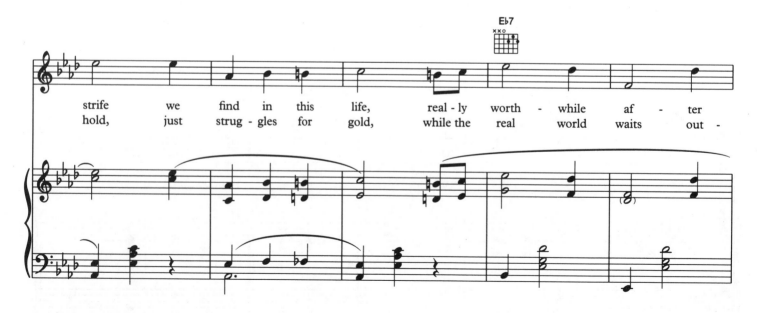

1. strife we find in this life, real - ly worth - while af - ter
2. hold, we just strug - gles for gold, while the real world waits out -

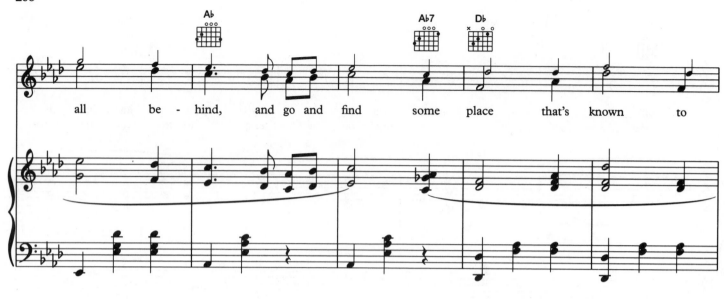

all be - hind, and go and find some place that's known to

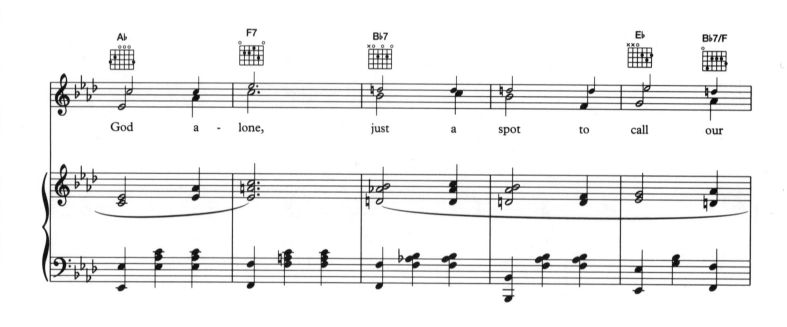

God a - lone, just a spot to call our

own. We'll find per-fect peace, where joys ne - ver cease, out

A LITTLE LOVE, A LITTLE KISS

Words by ADRIAN ROSS
Music by LAO SILESU

Allegretto moderato

1. When the scent-ed night of sum-mer cov - - ers field and ci - ty
2. Night will pass and day will fol - low af - - ter, oth - er griefs and
3. You and I may change like A - pril wea - - ther, oth - er loves may

with her veil of blue,_____ all the lanes are full of stray-ing
joys will come with day,_____ yet through all the weep-ing and the
call us, not in vain,_____ but to-night, at least, is ours to -

1   Dans Paris où tout n'est que folie
    Le désir nous hante un peu partout
    La femme nous parait plus jolie
    Elle sait nous rendre un peu plus fou
        Pour un peu d'amour, un peu d'amour
        Cet instant divin, mais bien trop court
        Car deux cœurs en cet instant suprême
        Se disent deux mots, deux seuls; je t'aime
        Moi, pour ces deux mots, ces mots d'amour
        Je donnerai bien mes nuits, mes jours
        Pour l'entendre en cet instant suprême
        Murmurer tout bas, tous bas; je t'aime!

2   L'on se fait souvent mille promesses
    Les femmes nous grisent de mots fous
    Mais qu'importe puisque leurs caresses
    Nous font passer des instants si doux
        Pour un peu . . .

LOOK FOR THE SILVER LINING

Words by B. G. DeSYLVA
Music by JEROME KERN

Boy: Please don't be of-fend-ed if I
Girl: As I wash my dish-es, I'll be

preach to you a while.
fol - low-ing your plan,

Tears are out of place in eyes
till I see the bright-ness in

that were meant to smile.
ev - 'ry pot and pan.

There's a way to make your ver - y
I am sure your point of view will

big - gest trou - bles small.
ease the dai - ly grind.

Here's the hap - py se - cret of it
So I'll keep re - peat-ing in my

all.
mind.

Refrain (*slowly, with warm expression*)

Look for the sil - ver lin - ing when-e'er a cloud ap -

p molto legato

LOVE'S OLD SWEET SONG

Words and Music by J. L. Molloy

Slowly

Once in the dear, dead days be-yond re-call, When on the world the
E-ven to-day we hear love's song of yore, Deep in our hearts it

mists be-gan to fall, Out of the dreams that rose in hap-py throng,
dwells for-ev-er-more, Foot-steps may fal - ter, wea-ry grow the way,

Low to our hearts love sang an old sweet song, And in the dusk where
Still we can hear it at the close of day, So 'til the end when

fell the fire-light gleam, Soft-ly it wove it-self in-to our dream.
life's dim shad-ows fall, Love will be found the sweet-est song of all.

Love's Old Sweet Song - 2 - 1

LITTLE GREY HOME IN THE WEST

Words by DOROTHY EARDLEY-WILMOT
Music by HERMANN LOHR

1. When the gol-den sun sinks in the hills, _____ and the
(2.) hands that will wel-come me in, _____ there are

toil of a long day is o'er, _____ though the road may be long, in the
lips I am burn-ing to kiss, _____ there are two eyes that shine just be -

1.

Bb/D *rit.* Bdim7 Cm6 F7 *a tempo* Bb Gm Cm7

lit - tle grey home in the west._____

rit. *a tempo*

mf

F13 Bbmaj7 Eb F7 Bb

2. There are

mf

2. **molto rall.**

Bb/D Bdim7 Cm6 F13 Bb

lit - tle grey home in the west._____

molto rall.

p

LOVE WILL FIND A WAY

Words by HARRY GRAHAM
Music by HAROLD FRASER-SIMSON

LOVE, HERE IS MY HEART

Words by ADRIAN ROSS
Music by LAO SILESU

1. I have ga - thered my heart as a rose, _____ as a
2. I have spo - ken my heart in a song, _____ in a

rose from the mid - sum - mer gar - den, and my love at the heart of it
song of the night - in - gale's trill - ing, for she sang to me all the night

MARCHETA

Words and Music by VICTOR SCHERTZINGER

MARGIE

Words by BENNY DAVIS
Music by CON CONRAD
and J. RUSSEL ROBINSON

Margie - 2 - 1

MARY'S A GRAND OLD NAME

Words and Music by GEORGE M. COHAN

MEET ME IN ST. LOUIS, LOUIS

Lyrics by ANDREW B. STERLING
Additional Lyrics by TIMOTHY GRAY
Music by KERRY MILLS

MEMORIES

Words by GUS KAHN
Music by EGBERT VAN ALSTYNE

1. Round me at twi - light come steal - ing,_____
2. Sun - light may teach me for - get - ting,_____

sha - dows of days that are gone._____
noon - light brings thoughts that are new._____

M-O-T-H-E-R
(A Word That Means The World To Me)

Lyrics by HOWARD JOHNSON
Music by THEODORE MORSE

M-O-T-H-E-R - 2 - 2

MOTHER MACHREE

Words by RIDA JOHNSON YOUNG
Music by CHAUNCEY OLCOTT and ERNEST R. BALL

MY MAMMY
(The Sun Shines East – The Sun Shines West)

Words by SAM LEWIS and JOE YOUNG
Music by WALTER DONALDSON

I'se ___ a - com - in' ___ sor - ry that I made you wait,

I'se ___ a - com - in' ___ hope and pray I'm not too late,

Mam - my, Mam - my, ___ I'd walk a

mil - lion miles for one of your smiles, MY MAM - - MY. MY.

MY MELANCHOLY BABY

Words by GEORGE A NORTON
and MAYBELLE E WATSON
Music by ERNIE BURNETT

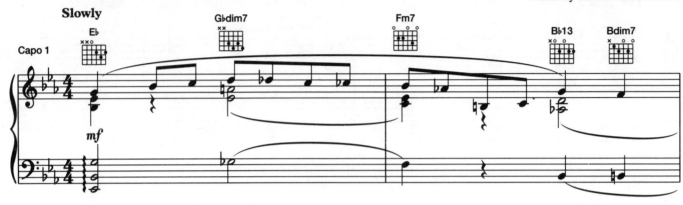

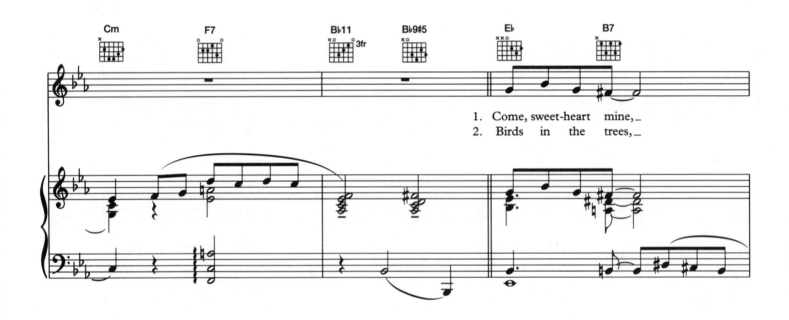

1. Come, sweet-heart mine,_
2. Birds in the trees,_

don't sit and pine,_ tell me of the cares that make you feel so blue.
sweet me - lo - dies,_ they will take you to a land of peace - ful dreams.

Ev-ery cloud must have a sil-ver lin - ing, wait un-til the

sun shines through._____ Smile, my hon-ey dear, while I

kiss a - way each tear, or else I shall be mel-an-cho-ly

too._____ too._____

MOONLIGHT BAY

Words by EDWARD MADDEN
Music by PERCY WENRICH

254

MY GAL SAL

Words and Music by PAUL DRESSER

MY SWEETHEART'S THE MAN IN THE MOON

Words and Music by JAMES THORNTON

My Sweetheart's The Man In The Moon - 2 - 1

Chorus, Waltz tempo

My sweet heart's the man in the moon _____ I'm go-ing to mar-ry him soon _____ 'Twould fill me with bliss just to give him one kiss, But I know that a doz-en I nev-er would miss, I'll go up in a great big bal-loon _____ And see my sweet-heart in the moon, _____ Then be-hind a dark cloud, where no one is al-low'd, I'll make love to the man in the moon. _____

My Sweetheart's The Man In The Moon - 2 - 2

MY WILD IRISH ROSE

Words and Music by CHAUNCEY OLCOTT

She is dear-er by far than the world's bright-est star, And I call her my wild I-rish Rose.

And my one wish has been that some day I may win The heart of my wild I-rish Rose.

REFRAIN *With much expression*

My wild I-rish Rose, The sweet-est flow'r that grows, You may search ev-'ry-where but none can com-pare With my wild I-rish Rose. My wild I-rish Rose, The dear-est flow'r that grows And some day for my sake, she may let me take The bloom from my wild I-rish Rose.

OH! YOU BEAUTIFUL DOLL

Words by A SEYMOUR BROWN
Music by NAT D AYER

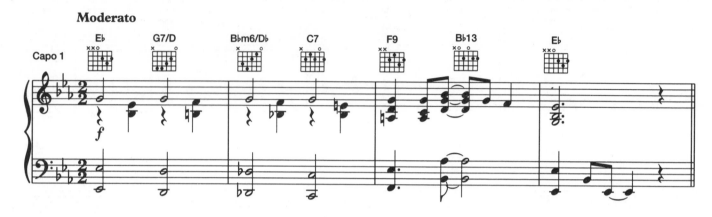

1. Hon - ey dear,___ want you near,___ just turn out the light and then come
2. Pre - cious prize,___ close your eyes,___ now we're goin' to vi - sit lov - ers'

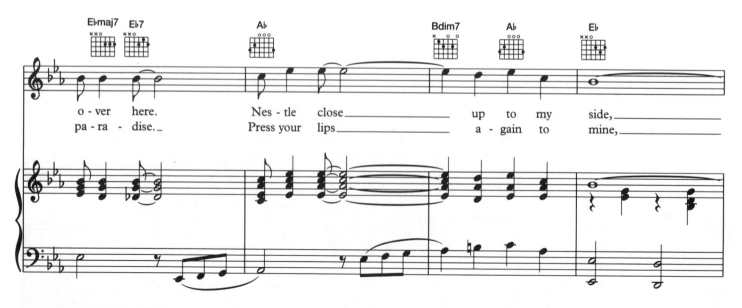

o - ver here. Nes - tle close_____ up to my side,_____
pa - ra - dise.___ Press your lips_____ a - gain to mine,_____

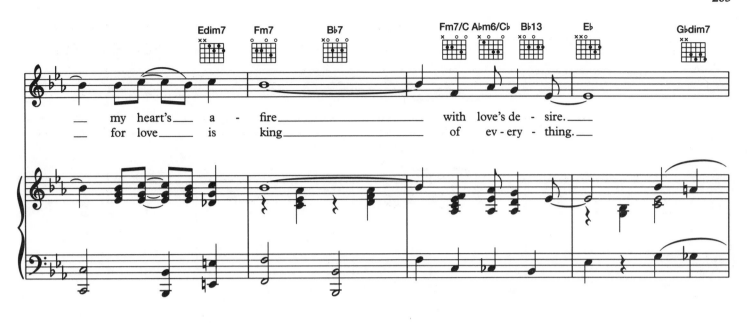

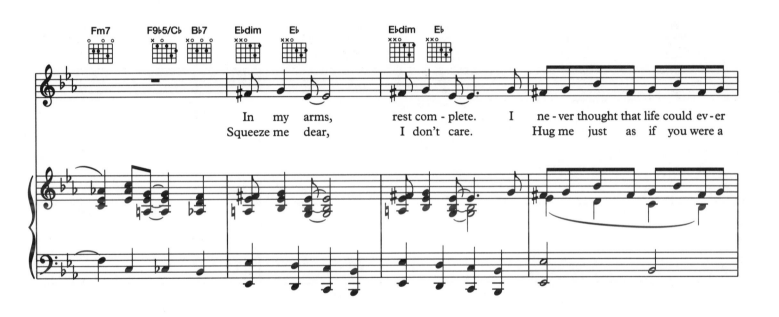

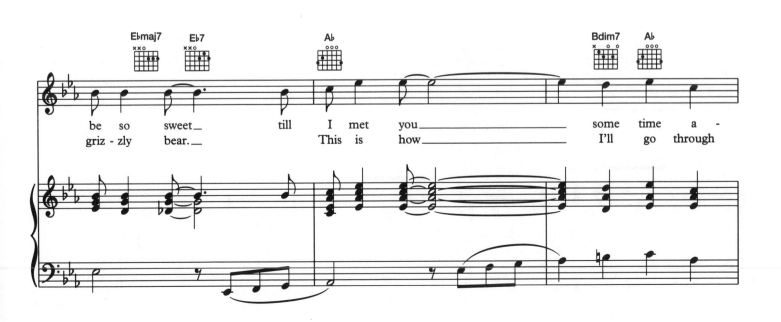

- go, _____ but now _____ you know, _____ I love you so. _____
life, _____ no care _____ or strife, _____ when you're my wife.

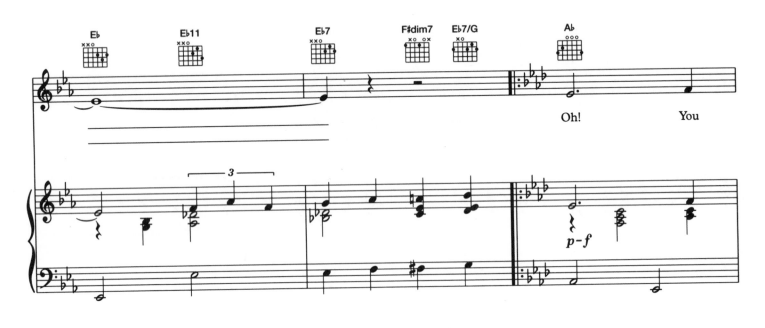

Oh! You

beau-ti-ful doll, _ you great big beau-ti-ful doll! ____ Let ____ me put my

OH, JOHNNY OH

Words by ED ROSE
Music by ABE OLMAN

ON TOP OF OLD SMOKY

Traditional

Moderato

1. On top of old Smok - y, _____ All cov - er'd with
2. For a thief, he'll just rob you, _____ And take what you

snow, _____ I lost my true lov - er, _____
have, _____ But a false heart - ed lov - er _____

For court - in' too slow. _____ 2. For court - in's great
Will send you to your grave. _____ 4. She'll hug you and

5.

The grave will decay you
Will turn you to dust,
Not one boy in a hundred
A poor girl can trust.

6.

They'll tell you they love you
To give your heart ease,
As soon as your back's turned
They'll court as they please.

On Top Of Old Smoky - 2 - 2

OVER THERE

Words and Music by GEORGE M. COHAN

Over There - 3 - 1

ON THE ROAD TO MANDALAY

Words and Music by OLEY SPEAKS
(From Kipling's "Barrack Room Ballads")

By the old Moul-mein Pa-go-da look-in' east-ward to the sea, There's a Bur-ma girl a-

PACK UP YOUR TROUBLES IN YOUR OLD KIT BAG AND SMILE, SMILE, SMILE

Words by GEORGE ASAF
Music by FELIX POWELL

A PARADISE FOR TWO

Words by CLIFFORD HARRIS
and ARTHUR VALENTINE
Music by JAMES W TATE

1. There's no song with-in my heart,
(2.) Fate may some-times prove un-kind,

but of love for you,
yet though skies are grey,

yet we must re-
ev-ery cloud is

PEG O' MY HEART

Words by ALFRED BRYAN
Music by FRED FISHER

THE PIPES OF PAN ARE CALLING

Words by ARTHUR WIMPERIS
Music by LIONEL MONCKTON

1. With a me - lo - dy en - thral - ling,
2. Loud they laugh be - side the foun - tain,

loud the wood - land e - choes ring.
shrill they min - gle with the breeze,

PRETTY BABY

Words by GUS KAHN
Music by TONY JACKSON and EGBERT VAN ALSTYNE

Ev-'ry-bod-y loves a ba-by that's why I'm in love with you, Pret-ty Ba - by, Pret-ty Ba - by; And I'd like to be your sis-ter, broth-er, dad and moth-er too, Pret-ty Ba - by, Pret-ty Ba - by. Won't you come and let me rock you in my cra-dle of love,_ And we'll cud-dle all the time._ Oh! I want a Lov-in' Ba-by and it might as well be you, Pret-ty Ba-by of mine._ Ev-'ry- mine._

POOR BUTTERFLY

Words by JOHN L. GOLDEN
Music by RAYMOND HUBBELL

PUT YOUR ARMS AROUND ME, HONEY

Words by JUNIE McCREE
Music by ALBERT VON TILZER

it's with you dear, That I love to be._____

moon-y, loon-y, But my love' is true._____

CHORUS.

Put your arms a-round me hon-ey, hold me tight,

Hud-dle up and cud-dle up with all your might,

Oh, babe, Won't you roll dem eyes, Eyes that

PUT ON YOUR OLD GREY BONNET

Words by STANLEY MURPHY
Music by PERCY WENRICH

G7

stern old heart it light-en'd, As he turn'd to her and said, _____

cou-ple lay a dream-ing Dream-ing of the words he said; _____

C7 **F**

CHORUS. **Bb** **Eb** **Bb**

"Put on your old grey bon-net with the blue rib-bon on it, While I hitch old

p-f

C7 **F7** **Bb** **D7** **Gm** **Eb**

Dob-bin to the shay, _____ And through the fields of clo-ver. We'll drive up to

Bb **C7** **F7** **Bb** 1 2

Do-ver on our gold-en Wed-ding day." _____ "Put on your _____

f

RAGTIME COWBOY JOE

Words by GRANT CLARKE
Music by LEWIS F. MUIR and MAURICE ABRAHAMS

cows and sheep— / dance hall floor— Ev-'ry night they say he sings the herd to sleep / No one but a lu-na-tic would start a war,

In a bass-o rich and deep— / Wise men know— his for-ty four— Croon-ing soft and low. _____ / Makes men dance for fair. _____

Chorus, Moderately

He al-ways sings rag-gy mu-sic to the cat-tle, as he swings back and

for-ward in the sad-dle, on a horse that is syn-co-pat-ed, gait-ed, and there's

Ragtime Cowboy Joe - 3 - 2

Ragtime Cowboy Joe · 3 · 3

ROSE ROOM

Words by HARRY WILLIAMS
Music by ART HICKMAN

ROSES OF PICARDY

Words by FREDERICK E WEATHERLY
Music by HAYDN WOOD

ROCK-A-BYE YOUR BABY WITH A DIXIE MELODY

Words by SAM LEWIS and JOE YOUNG
Music by JEAN SCHWARTZ

SCHOOL DAYS
(When We Were A Couple Of Kids)

Words by WILL D. COBB
Music by GUS EDWARDS

School Days - 3 - 1

School Days - 3 - 2

School Days - 3 - 3

SHE IS MA DAISY

Words by HARRY LAUDER and J. D. HARPER
Music by HARRY LAUDER

THE SIDEWALKS OF NEW YORK
(East Side, West Side)

Words by CHARLES B. LAWLER
Music by JAMES W. BLAKE

SHINE ON HARVEST MOON

Words by JACK NORWORTH
Music by NORA BAYES

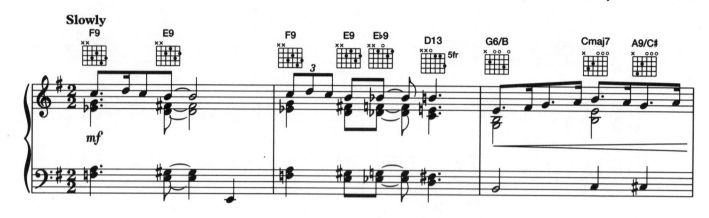

1. The night was might - y dark, so you could hard - ly see,___ for the
2. I can't see why a boy should sigh, when by his side___ is the

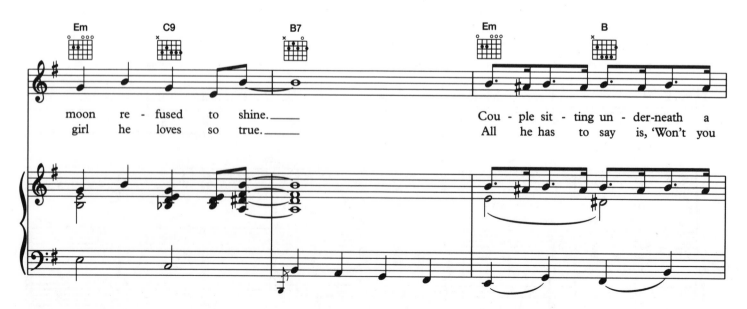

moon re - fused to shine.___ Cou - ple sit - ting un - der-neath a
girl he loves so true.___ All he has to say is, 'Won't you

SMILES

Words by J. WILL. CALLAHAN
Music by LEE S. ROBERTS

SMILIN' THROUGH

Words and Music by ARTHUR PENN

SOME OF THESE DAYS

Words and Music by SHELTON BROOKS

sweet-hearts in a coun-try town, the neigh-bours say,__ lived hap-pi-ly the whole day
went a-way, and from that day the world's been sad,__ he re-al-iz-es his mis-

long, un-til one day he told her he must go a-way,__ she
-take. He lis-tened to the gos-sips, and that's al-ways bad,__ she for

THE SONG OF SONGS

English Words by CLARENCE LUCAS
French Words by MAURICE VAUCAIRE
Music by MOYA

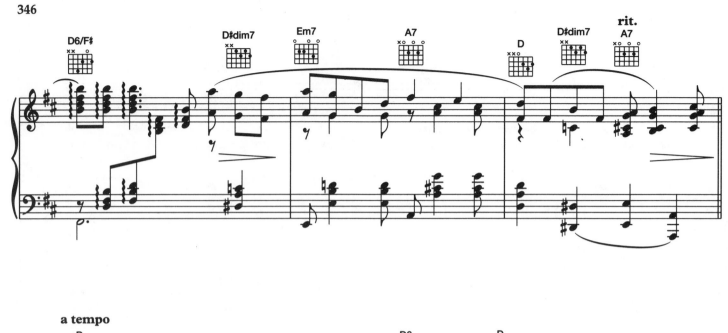

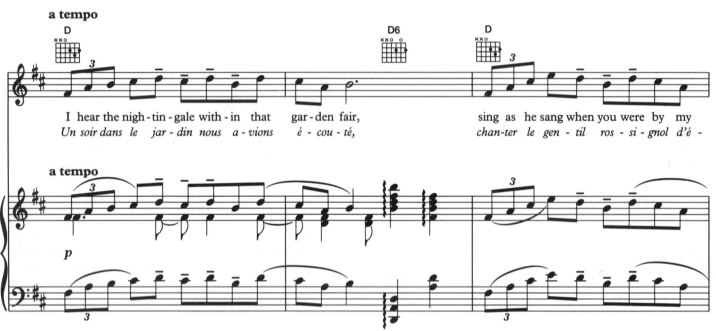

I hear the nigh-tin-gale with-in that gar-den fair, sing as he sang when you were by my

Un soir dans le jar-din nous a-vions é-cou-té, chan-ter le gen-til ros-si-gnol d'é-

side. I see your eyes re-veal the love no words can tell, and I

-té, cet in-ter-mède en-i-vrait la nuit tié-de, tes pa-

SUNSHINE OF YOUR SMILE

Words by LESLIE LEONARD COOKE
Music by LILIAN RAY

1. Dear face that holds so sweet a smile for me, were you not mine, how dark this world would be. I know no
2. Sha-dows may fall a-cross the land and sea, sun-shine from all the world may hid-den be, but I shall

SWEET ADELINE

Words by RICHARD H. GERARD
Music by HARRY ARMSTRONG

SWANEE

Words by IRVING CAESAR
Music by GEORGE GERSHWIN

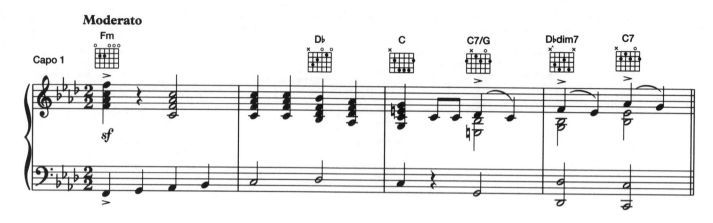

I've been a-way from you a long time,_____

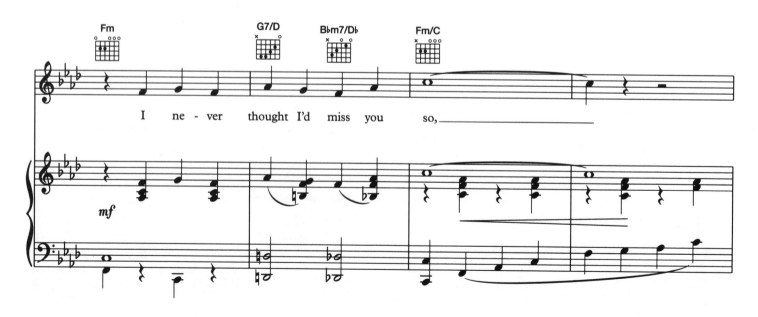

I ne-ver thought I'd miss you so,_____

Francis Day & Hunter Ltd, London WC2H 0EA and Warner/Chappell Music Ltd, London W1Y 3FA

SWEET ROSIE O'GRADY

360

Words and Music by MAUD NUGENT

THE SWEETEST STORY EVER TOLD

Words and Music by R. M. STULTS

SYMPATHY

Words by OTTO A HARBACH and GUS KAHN
Music by RUDOLF FRIML

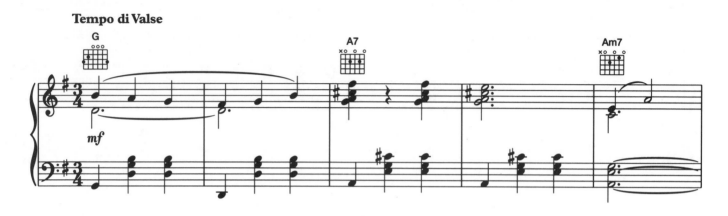

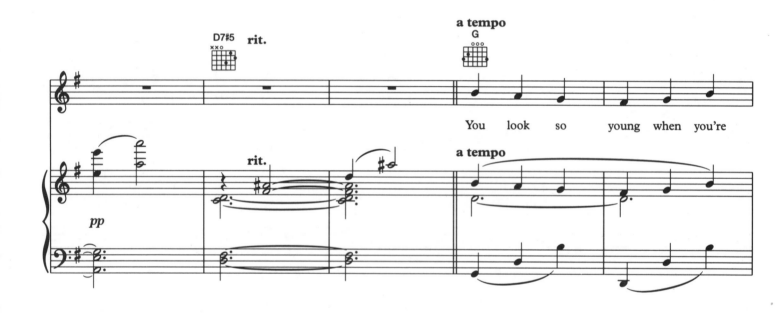

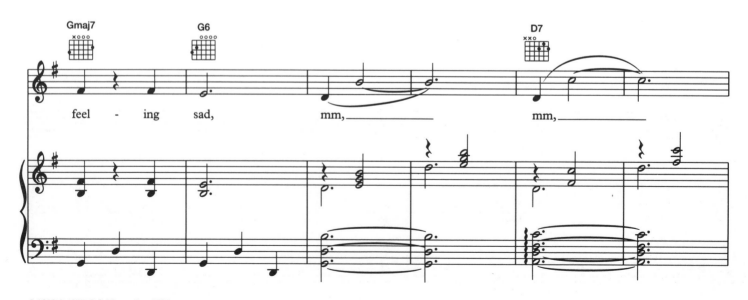

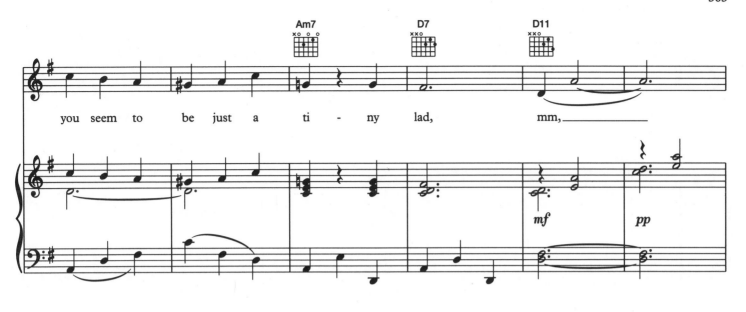

you seem to be just a ti - ny lad, mm, _____

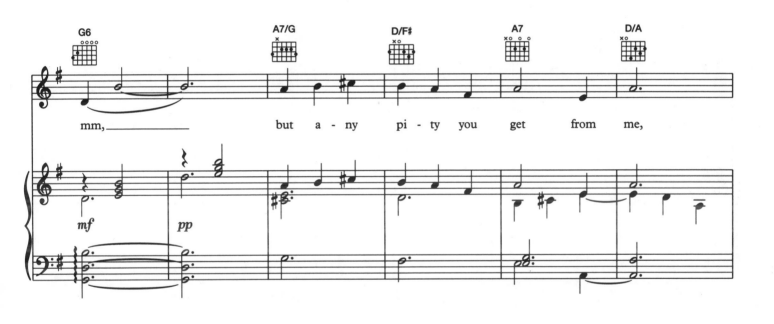

mm, _____ but a - ny pi - ty you get from me,

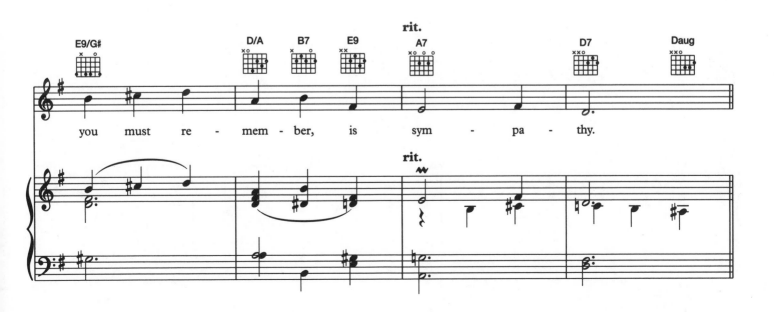

you must re - mem - ber, is sym - pa - thy.

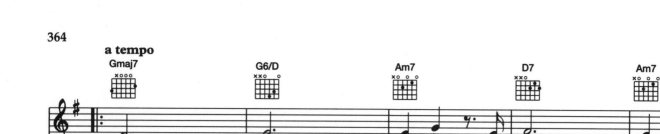

You need sym - pa - thy, sym - pa-
I need sym - pa - thy, sym - pa-

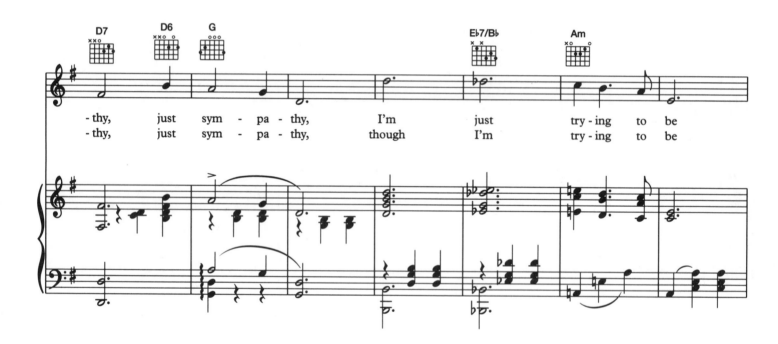

- thy, just sym - pa - thy, I'm just try - ing to be
- thy, just sym - pa - thy, though I'm try - ing to be

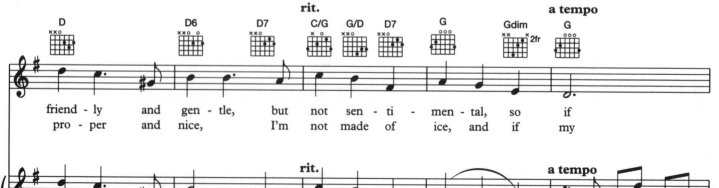

friend - ly and gen - tle, but not sen - ti - men - tal, so if
pro - per and nice, I'm not made of ice, and if my

TA-RA-RA BOOM-DER-É

Words and Music by HENRY J. SAYERS
Arranged by Elmer Schoebel

THAT'S AN IRISH LULLABY
(Too-Ra-Loo-Ra-Loo-Ral)

Music and words by J. R. SHANNON

TAKE ME OUT TO THE BALL GAME

Words by JACK NORWORTH
Music by ALBERT VON TILZER

Take me out to the ball game

Take me out to the crowd. _____

TIGER RAG
(Hold That Tiger!)

Words by HARRY DE COSTA
Music by ORIGINAL DIXIELAND JAZZ BAND

Choke him, poke him, kick him and soak him! Where's that Ti - ger? Where's that

Ti - ger? Where, _____ oh where can he be? _____

Low or High - brow, They all cry now. "Please play that

Ti - ger Rag for me." _____ me." _____

TILL WE MEET AGAIN

Words by RAYMOND B. EGAN
Music by RICHARD A. WHITING

Moderate Waltz tempo

Smile the while you kiss me sad a - dieu,

When the clouds roll by I'll come to you; Then the

skies will seem more blue Down in lov - ers

TWO LITTLE BOYS

Words by EDWARD MADDEN
Music by THEODORE MORSE

VIENNA, CITY OF MY DREAMS

Words and Music by RUDOLF SIECZYNSKI
English Words by EDWARD LOCKTON

1. My heart sees her yet, my heart can't for - get, Vi -
1. *Mein Herz und mein Sinn schwärmt stets nur für Wien, für*

-en - na, dear ci - ty of dreams._____ In vi - sions of night, I
Wien wie es weint, wie es lacht,_____ da kenn ich mich aus, da

see ev - ery light, each case - ment of fai - ry - land gleams,_____ a -
bin ich halt z'Haus bei Tag und noch mehr bei der Nacht,_____ und

WEE WEE MARIE

Words by ALFRED BRYAN and JOE McCARTHY
Music by FRED FISCHER

WHEN IRISH EYES ARE SMILING

Words by CHAUNCEY OLCOTT
and GEORGE GRAFF JR
Music by ERNEST R BALL

WAIT TILL THE SUN SHINES, NELLIE

Words by ANDREW B. STERLING
Music by HARRY VON TILZER

WHEN IT'S APPLE BLOSSOM TIME IN NORMANDY

Written and Composed by Mellor Gifford and Trevor

WHEN THE SAINTS GO MARCHING IN

Traditional

1. Oh, when the saints _____ go march - ing
2. (Oh, when the) sun _____ re - fuse to
3. (Oh, when they) crown _____ Him Lord of
4. (Oh, when they) gath - - - er 'round the

in, _____ Oh, when the saints go march - ing
shine, _____ Oh, when the sun re - fuse to
All, _____ Oh, when the crown Him Lord of
throne, _____ Oh, when the gath - er 'round the

When The Saints Go Marching In - 2 - 1

When The Saints Go Marching In - 2 - 2

WHEN YOU WORE A TULIP

Words by JACK MAHONEY
Music by PERCY WENRICH

WILL YOU LOVE ME IN DECEMBER
(As You Do In May?)

Words by JAMES J. WALKER
Music by ERNEST R. BALL

Will you love me in De-cem-ber as you do in May, Will you love me in the good old fash-ioned way?_____ When my hair has all turned gray, Will you kiss me then, and say, That you love me in De-cem-ber as you do in May?

YOU CAN'T STOP THE YANKS

Words and Music by JACK CADDIGAN and CHICK STORY

THE YANKEE DOODLE BOY

Words and Music by GEORGE M. COHAN

YOU MADE ME LOVE YOU

Words by JOE McCARTHY
Music by JAMES MONACO

YOU'RE A GRAND OLD FLAG

Words and Music by GEORGE M. COHAN

Marcato

You're a grand old flag, You're a high fly - ing flag, And for-

ev - er in peace, may you wave. You're the em - blem

of the land I love, The home of the free and the

You're A Grand Old Flag - 2 - 1

YOU TELL ME YOUR DREAM
(I'll Tell You Mine)

Words and Music by GUS KAHN and CHAS N. DANIELS

You Tell Me Your Dream - 3 - 1

414

sweet, dear, with love di - vine

Why keep me wait - ing, why let me

pine You tell me your dream,

I'll tell you mine. mine.

You Tell Me Your Dream - 3 - 3

100 YEARS OF POPULAR MUSIC

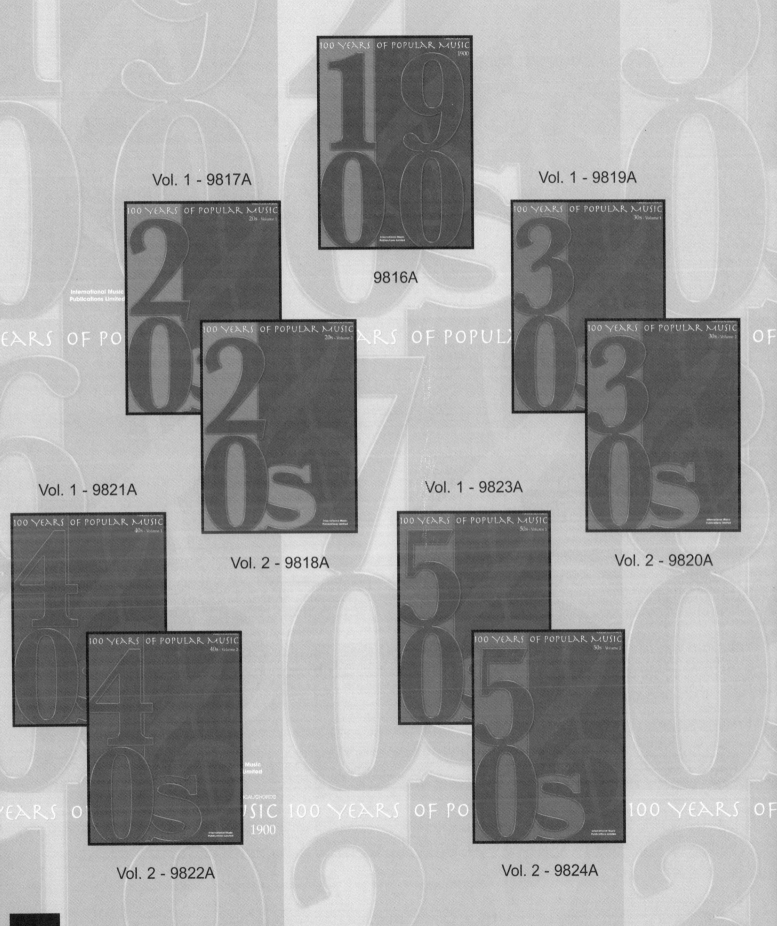

Vol. 1 - 9817A

9816A

Vol. 1 - 9819A

Vol. 1 - 9821A

Vol. 1 - 9823A

Vol. 2 - 9818A

Vol. 2 - 9820A

Vol. 2 - 9822A

Vol. 2 - 9824A

International
MUSIC
Publications

IMP's Exciting New Series!

100 YEARS OF POPULAR MUSIC

Vol. 1 - 9825A

Vol. 1 - 9827A

Vol. 1 - 9829A

Vol. 1 - 9831A

Vol. 2 - 9826A

Vol. 2 - 9828A

Vol. 2 - 9830A

Vol. 2 - 9832A

Vol. 2 - 9833A

IMP
International
MUSIC
Publications

IMP's Exciting New Series!